Dedications

To Mum and Dad, Margie, Bert, Joan, John, Lee, Fred, Margaret, Helen, Kate, David, Alex and family.

Jason, Jodie, Gerry, Yazmin, Reece, Mason, Ronnie, Tayler, Mollie, Terry, Glen, Alex, Alina and all the family.

Diane, Ralph, and family, Martin Seager and family, Vyash Junglee and all friends.

Special thank you to Claire Voet of Blossom Spring publishing.

First Published in 2021 by Blossom Spring Publishing

Little Astral Dogs© 2021 Leslie Jenkins

ISBN 978-1-8384972-1-7

E: admin@blossomspringpublishing.com

W: www.blossomspringpublishing.com

Little Astral Dogs

by Leslie Jenkins

Angel

My name is Angel, and I'm by my master's side
I love him dearly and I will always be your guide.
I never bark unless you're in distress,
I will protect you always, you are the best.

We have so many adventures
And today we go to the park.
We go to our favourite cafe,
And play until dark.

Today we listen to the radio
In the garden by the flowers,
We enjoy the sun together
For these are our golden hours.

Naughty Dan

Sausages in the pan,
Sausages on the floor
It's naughty Dan
In trouble once more!

Chewed up slippers and
Chewed up shoes
Chewed up newspaper and
There is no news.

Naughty Dan
We love you heaps
Behind the sofa
Dan now sleeps.

Betty Diamond

My name is Betty diamond,
And I live in Belgrave Square.
So beautiful is my house,
You will stop and stare!

For I am exquisite as you can see,
The other dogs do not speak
And they are rude to me.
Jealousy of course rules the day,
But I have good manners in every single way.
Champagne for breakfast
Champagne for tea
For I am Betty Diamond
The queen of luxury.

Rover To The Rescue

In the boat we set sail,
Feeling happy and I wag my tail.
We see a child struggling in the sea
So I will jump in to rescue thee

For I am Rover, the rescue dog
Swimming bravely through the fog.
Now we are safe on the land and,
With more help at hand!

Thank you Lord, for helping me,
Your guiding light brings us home for tea.

Sporty Dog

I am a sportsman in disguise
I will take you by surprise
Into the pond I will splash
Then out of the pond like a flash

I have found an old bike tyre
And chew it to my heart's desire

Home bound time for dinner
Running through the park, I am the winner,
I am a sportsman in disguise,
I will always take you by surprise.

Ollie The Sheepdog

Over the hills I guide our sheep

Then I settle down to sleep

My master calls "Ollie it's time to go"

So, one more time we are on with the show.

It starts to rain, but there's work to do,

Ollie the sheepdog it's down to you,

So safely back to the fold

I must be strong, I must be bold.

I love my work and my master too

So happy to serve and be with you.

The Fortune Teller

I will tell you your future
I will make you smile
Please listen to me
Just for a little while.

As I gaze into the crystal ball
You're jumping in the sea
Adventure is shown
On the path of your destiny.

Be kind, be happy
In all the things you do
Remember my words
And I'll always be with you.

Crackers My Dog

Who is the one who ate my shoe?
Who is the one that trod in the glue?
Who is the one who ate my vindaloo?
Crackers my dog and I love you.

Who is the one who barks at the door?
Who is the one who got mud on the floor?
Who is the one who ate the coleslaw?
Crackers my dog and I love you.

Who is the one that was there when I cried?
Who is the one that knows that I tried?
Who is the one that is always by my side?
Crackers my dog and I love you!

Doggies In The Sky

I love you master when you stroke my head,
When I sleep with you at the end of your bed
But now is my time to say goodbye,
I travel to meet the doggies in the sky.

Do not be sad on this day
For I am only a breath away
Our love is there for all our time
There is no death its spirit divine.

Our life together for all these years
Are golden,
So please no tears,
But now it's time to say goodbye
Be happy I'm safe, with the doggies in the sky.

Charisma

I came home from work today,
I came home and cried
You licked my hand and so glad you're by my side

We shared our dinner together as we are broke
We share our life together alone in the smoke
We safely sleep under my cloak

Your love for me is always real
Your love for me is the real deal

You maybe a dog but you are a true friend
With you my little dog there's no pretend,
Soul mates together till the end

Charisma is your name and together we stand
Charisma is your name as we listen to the band

Charisma is your name as we go the promise land.

Apollo

As I gaze at the stars tonight
My mistress reads by candlelight
Imagine I see a dog in the sky
Now I have a tear in my eye
I miss Apollo my dear, dear, friend
Who lived with us until the end?
But then I see a smiling face
It's Apollo looking at me from outer space
So now I know he's safe and sound
Happiness and peace we have both found.

Neptune

I am a dog who loves to laugh
I am a dog who loves a bath
See me now bury my bone
Now I am on the telephone

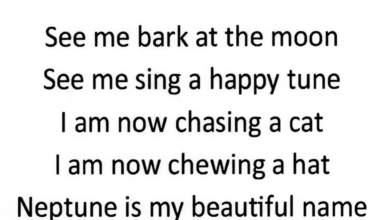

See me bark at the moon
See me sing a happy tune
I am now chasing a cat
I am now chewing a hat
Neptune is my beautiful name

The Astral Dog

I love to roll in the mud and be dirty
My mistress calls "oh Bertie! Bertie!
Mud everywhere all on your paws
And all over my lovely clean floors."
I clean myself and settle to sleep
I curl up quietly then have a peep
The naughty cats are up the tree
But don't worry they don't bother me

So, I now retire and look at the stars
Is that Jupiter or is that Mars?
For I am the Astral Dog
As I sleep by the fire and the crackling Log

I hear the grandfather clock striking the hour
I can smell a rose my favourite flower
In the distance I hear a cat meow

The Battersea Dog

Little dog don't feel depressed
Just think of the best
A home for you and me
By the beautiful sea
Yes my little Battersea Dog

So you have found your home
There's no need to be alone
For you are now safe with me
Don't feel afraid let it be
My little Battersea Dog.

JUDY
MY BEAUTIFUL DOG

I always wanted a dog so, when I was seven years old my mother agreed. We set off to Battersea dog's home in 1961. Sadly, all the dogs were large and the only two puppies were two Labradors; one black Labrador, who was in quarantine and the other golden Labrador was promised to a blind man.

I came away disappointed, but my mum said, "never mind!" As we rode on the 243 bus in Tottenham north London, there was a small pet shop near the police station called **'Archers Pet Store'**. It was there we bought a beautiful little mongrel puppy, golden and white, with beautiful brown eyes. We rode home on the bus. We were so excited. When my father came home, my little dog was sitting on his favourite armchair. Tell her "she can't stay" said my mum to my dad. My dad replied, "ah! She's so lovely and of course she can stay." The next day, still with no name for my little puppy, a young girl, my neighbour, asked "what are you calling your dog, Leslie?" I replied, "I don't know." "Call her Judy" said the girl. "Yes! Thank you."

So, she became Judy Jenkins.

I loved Judy, we played in the garden every day and she was my world. But one day she disappeared, my mother and I were so upset, as somehow in the garden she had got out very quickly. My father visited the local police station in Wood Green, in those days the police van would pick up stray dogs. The sergeant showed my father only two dogs – "No!" said my father "never mind." Another policeman called out, "Fred what about that little one in the boiler room" and low and behold it was Judy! My dad cried and Judy went absolutely potty seeing him again. Judy returned home safely.

I had to stay with my sister as my mum was in hospital and my father had to work. So, we stayed in my sister's flat for a few weeks. One day the washing machine overflowed. My sister was frantic and Judy seeing all the water filling the kitchen floor, thought it was wonderful and raced around the kitchen much to my sister's horror.

Judy was my first and only dog, I loved her dearly and sadly she became unwell and passed away. My mum said, "don't worry, she will be safe with all the other doggies in the sky." And I believe that, so my little poem is in this book for you to read and it is for all those who have lost their little doggie. Judy was a kind, beautiful and spiritual dog that was always by my side. So, she really belongs in the memory hall of astral dogs.

About the Author

Leslie Jenkins was born in Muswell Hill, London. He is married with a family and still lives in London today. He is a qualified private English TEFL teacher and trained actor with RADA and Sylvia Young Theatre School.

His first book **Astral Cats** was published in 2017 and has two recent children's books published, **Mrs Jacaranda Stories** also by Blossom Spring Publishing.

www.blossomspringpublishing.com

Printed in Great Britain
by Amazon